SNAKES

A QUANTUM BOOK

Published by Grange Books
an imprint of Grange Books Plc
The Grange
Kingsnorth Industrial Estate
Hoo, nr. Rochester
Kent ME3 9ND

ISBN 1-84013-145-4

This book is produced by
Quantum Books Ltd
6 Blundell Street
London N7 9BH

Project Manager: Rebecca Kingsley
Project Editor: Judith Millidge
Design/Editorial: David Manson
Andy McColm, Maggie Manson

The material in this publication previously appeared in
*Book of Snakes, Snakes of the World, Exotic Pet Survival
Guide*

QUMSPSN
Set in Futura
Reproduced in Singapore by Eray Scan
Printed in Singapore by Star Standard Industries (Pte) Ltd

Contents

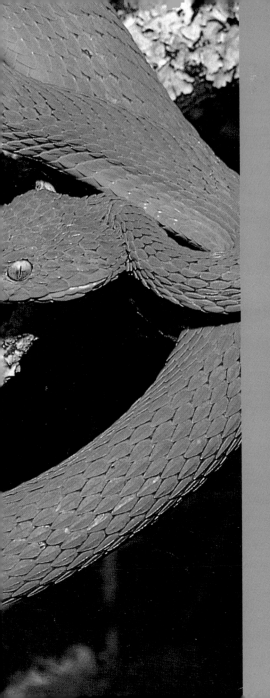

SUPERNATURAL SNAKES

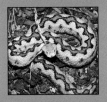

Snakes have always held a great fascination for people, which has often bordered on an obsession. Since prehistoric times, snakes have been shrouded in mysticism and superstition. This fascination is due at least partly to their very strange shape and motion and their ability to strike unexpectedly with deadly accuracy. With such inhuman and 'unnatural' attributes people considered them to be supernatural and superhuman.

Snakes through History

Myths and legends about snakes abound, and they have been worshipped and used in ceremonies and rituals all over the world. The aborigines in Australia, who still practise rock painting, frequently depict snakes.

ANCIENT SNAKES

In the Bible, Adam and Eve are tricked by the serpent in the Garden of Eden into eating fruit from the tree of knowledge and consequently the Judeo-Christian view of the serpent is one of evil. By contrast, in ancient Egypt, snakes were revered as gods.

Egypt's economy depended on the Nile, and the Spirit of the Nile was a snake god. The snake symbolised the mighty power of the ruling Pharaoh. The most famous snake in Egypt was the asp, supposedly used in the suicide of Cleopatra, possibly an Egyptian Cobra or poisonous viper.

Left. The harmless Milk Snake mimics the warning colouration of the dangerous, highly poisonous coral snakes.

Above. The colours of the Texas Coral Snake provide a clear warning that the snake is dangerously venomous.

SNAKES IN MEDICINE

Eating the flesh of snakes is often thought to cure or at least prevent disease. The Chinese eat snakes as a cure for tuberculosis and in the US, rattlesnake oil was sold as a remedy. Snake venom has been used as a cure for gangrene, meningitis, cholera and as a blood coagulant. In 293 BC, a Roman plague was cured by the god of medicine, Aesculapius, who appeared in the form of a snake. Even today, the emblem of the medical profession is a staff with two entwined snakes.

SNAKEBITES

It is estimated that about 30,000 people worldwide die each year from snakebites mostly in poorer countries without medical care. In India, 10,000 people a year die from bites, in the US the number is less than 30. In Britain, you are more likely to die from a bee sting (6 a year) than a snakebite (1 since 1945). Snakebites can be prevented with a few simple precautions, such as not picking up unidentified snakes, being careful where you walk and also wearing adequate footwear.

Biology and Evolution

Long before humans and other mammals evolved, reptiles were spreading over all but the coldest parts of the world. Snakes are a highly successful group of reptiles that have colonised almost all habitats, since they first appeared at least 130 million years ago.

SNAKE BIOLOGY

Snakes have a number of features in common, making their biology rather consistent. They have all lost their limbs and their long cylinder-shaped bodies impose restrictions. All snakes are, to a greater or lesser extent, dependent on the warmth of the sun to maintain their temperature and to incubate their eggs or develop their young. Although some species are highly territorial, some have elaborate courtships and others hibernate communally, snakes generally lack the social behaviour found in many birds, mammals and other groups of animals.

Left. The Fox Snake from the Great Lakes region in the US is a powerful constrictor, killing its prey by suffocation.

Above. The Paradise Flying Tree Snake has attractive markings which also act as very effective camouflage.

SNAKE FOSSILS

The earliest fossil remains which are recognisably of a snake were found in 130 million-year-old rocks in the Sahara in North Africa. The largest snake fossil found was an extinct python in Egypt, which may have measured as much as 18 metres (60ft) in length.

Relatively few snake fossils have been found as most fossils are of marine creatures. Since snakes lived mostly on land few have been preserved as fossils.

SNAKE EVOLUTION

There is little doubt that snakes evolved from lizards with some transitional forms appearing in the Cretaceous period – the great age of the dinosaurs. It was not until after the end of the dinosaurs, 65 million years ago, that snakes started to diversify and even today their evolution is still progressing. In geological terms, the snakes are still a new group, but with some 2,700 varied species around the world.

Snake Senses

Snakes gather information about the world in a very different way from us. While we rely mainly on sight and hearing, these senses are very poorly developed in snakes. Instead they depend on other stimuli, in particular scents and in some cases, heat.

SNAKE HEARING

Snakes are said to be deaf, because they lack outer ears and Eustachian tubes, and are unable to receive airborne sound waves. However, their inner ear reacts acutely to any ground vibrations which are detected by the lower jaw, in contact with the ground, and transmitted via the bones.

SNAKE EYESIGHT

Snake eyes are usually inefficient. They are unable to change the shape of the lens of the eye to focus and, most have no movable eyelids giving them an unblinking stare. Those active in the day usually have rounded pupils while nocturnal snakes, such as pythons, have vertical slit pupils.

Left. The Fierce Snake, reputed to be the most poisonous snake in the world, is confined to desert regions of Australia.

Above. The White-Lipped Pit Viper's heat sensitive pits between eye and nostril can clearly be seen.

SNAKE SENSE OF SMELL

Smell is the most important sense to snakes. Prey, predators and members of the opposite sex are identified by the scent chemicals they emit. Scent particles from the air are picked up and 'tasted' by the snake's forked tongue. The information is then transferred to the brain via special scent-sensitive cells in the snake's palate.

HEAT-SEEKING SNAKES

All snakes are sensitive to changes in their surrounding temperature and to infra-red radiation. Some boas, pythons and all pit vipers have special heat receptors, or sensory pits, on each side of their head, between the eye and the nostril enabling them to detect and accurately strike at warm-blooded prey, even in total darkness.

Snake Locomotion

Although we say that snakes 'crawl', they can actually move in four ways: serpentine movement, concertina movement, rectilinear movement and sidewinding. The type of movement depends largely on the terrain.

SERPENTINE LOCOMOTION

In serpentine movement, the snake's body is bent into horizontal loops by the contraction of muscles on the inner side of each loop. As the contractions move along the snake, a series of waves passes from the head backwards. On land, serpentine motion is only possible where there are stones or vegetation on the ground for the waves to push against, propelling the snake forward.

CONCERTINA LOCOMOTION

Concertina movement is used when crawling over difficult terrain or in a confined space such as a small rodent's burrow. The snake wedges the back part of its body and extends the rest of the body forward as far as possible. It then wedges the head and concertinas the front of the body, drawing itself forward. The snake then wedges the back part again and repeats the process.

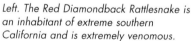

Left. The Red Diamondback Rattlesnake is an inhabitant of extreme southern California and is extremely venomous.

Above. The Speckled King Snake has an immunity to rattlesnake venom and they specialise in eating them.

RECTILINEAR LOCOMOTION

Rectilinear creeping is used by large heavy snakes, particularly boas and pythons, and allows them to move in a straight line. The snake uses the muscles joining the ventral scales to the ribs and contracts them in waves down the body. The ventral scales grip onto irregularities in the ground and the snake is propelled forward in a seemingly effortless gliding motion.

SIDEWINDING

Sidewinding relies least on a firm surface to push against and is used by snakes living in desert areas with shifting sand surfaces. In sidewinding, the snake shifts itself by moving sideways in a series of steps at an angle of about 45° to its body. The snake lifts its head off the ground and thrusts it to the side with the body following it in a series of parallel lines.

SNAKE SPECIES

Key to symbols
A number of icons are used to provide a snapshot of each snake. These are explained below.

Size (mm)

Habitat

 Grassy areas scrub and heath

Semi-aquatic

 Woodlands

Aquatic

 Tropical forests

Mountains and caves

 Desert and arid areas

Buildings

Diet

 Rodents and small mammals

Birds

 Fish and amphibians

Eggs

Danger!
Venomous
Several species produce venom that is toxic and very dangerous to humans.
Treat all snakes with caution.

SUNBEAM SNAKE

A shiny snake with smooth scales. The snout is shovel-shaped to allow the snake to burrow. The eyes are very small and round. The head is flattish. The underside is almost white, while the upperside is dark grey.

Scientific name *Xenopeltis unicolor.*
Size 1m (39in).
Habitat Agricultural areas, parks forests, under debris.
Distribution SE Asia.
Food Lizards, other snakes, frogs, small rodents.
Breeding Egg-laying, 6 egg clutches.

COMMON BOA

A large boa species with variable markings. They are grey or beige with dark brown markings along the back. It has no heat pits.

Scientific name *Boa constrictor.*
Size 4m (13ft).
Habitat Rain forest clearings, scrub, agricultural land, edges of villages.
Distribution S. and C America, W Indian islands.
Food Mammals and birds.
Breeding Live-bearing, up to 50 young in a litter.

PACIFIC BOA

This snake may be light grey, almost white with an irregular dark line running along its back, or brick-red with a maroon line. They can either be thick-set or slim. The head is flattish and the snout is obliquely angled. It lacks heat pits.

Scientific name *Candoia carinata.*
Size 1.5m (5ft).
Habitat Forests.
Distribution New Guinea.
Food Small mammals, birds, lizards.
Breeding Live-bearing, up to 70 young in a litter.

RUBBER BOA

A uniformly brown or olive coloured cylindrical snake, with small shiny scales and small eyes. The tail is short and blunt and is often raised off the ground to deflect attacks from its head.

Scientific name *Charina bottae.*
Size 80cm (32in).
Habitat Scrub, grassland, pinewood, beneath bark and trees.
Distribution N America.
Food Snakes, birds, small rodents, small salamanders.
Breeding Live-bearing, 2–8 in a litter.

EMERALD TREE BOA

The young snakes are red or orange, but the colour changes to green by the end of their first year of life. They have a row of white markings along their back and large prominent heat pits.

Scientific name *Corallus caninus*.
Size 1.6m (5¹/4ft).
Habitat Tropical rain forests with large trees.
Distribution Amazon Basin in S America.
Food Small mammals and birds.
Breeding Live-bearing, up to 20 in a litter.

1.6m

AMAZON TREE BOA

A slim snake whose colour varies from brown, yellow, orange or grey. Some varieties have dark markings on their backs. The young snakes are more brightly coloured than the adults. There are prominent heat pits.

Scientific name *Corallus enhydris*.
Size 1.8m (6ft).
Habitat Forests with tall trees.
Distribution S America, W Indies, Central America.
Food Small mammals, frogs, birds, lizards.
Breeding Live-bearing, up to 20 young.

1.8m

BRAZILIAN RAINBOW BOA

This is one of the most colourful of the nine subspecies of rainbow boa which exist. The scales are glossy and iridescent. There is a row of black circles down the back and black 'eyespots' along each side. It has shallow heat pits.

Scientific name *Epicrates cenchria cenchria*.
Size 2m (6^1/2ft).
Habitat Tropical forests and clearings.
Distribution S America.
Food Small mammals, birds.
Breeding Live-bearing, up to 30 young.

2m

HAITIAN BOA

A variable snake with blotches along the back. The colour of the blotches can be dark grey, brown or reddish. The ground colour is lighter, pale grey. There are shallow heat pits.

Scientific name *Epicrates striatus*.
Size 2.3m (7^1/2ft).
Habitat Forests and mangroves. Likes to climb up into thatched roofs.
Distribution Haiti, Bahamas.
Food Young eat lizards, adults eat chickens, small mammals, birds.
Breeding Live-bearing, up to 50 young.

2.3m

ROUGH-SCALED SAND BOA

The most attractively marked member of
this genus, with a distinctive dark
zigzag pattern running along the back.
The scales are raised, hence its name.
This is snake which frequently burrows
during the day.

Scientific name *Eryx conicus.*
Size 1m (39in).
Habitat Sandy, desert areas.
Distribution Sri Lanka, Pakistan,
India.
Food Rodents, birds, lizards.
Breeding Live-bearing, up to 11
young in a litter.

YELLOW ANACONDA

A snake with yellow colouring and an
attractive pattern of large black
blotches along the back and along the
flanks. The eyes point upwards. It has
no heat pits.

Scientific name *Eunectes notaeus.*
Size 2m (6^1/2ft).
Habitat Swamps.
Distribution S America.
Food Reptiles, birds, mammals.
Breeding Live-bearing, with large
litters.

BAJA CALIFORNIAN ROSY BOA

A heavily bodied snake with a narrow head and blunt tail. It has stripes running down the length of the body which are orange or brownish-orange and well-defined. The eyes are also orange. There are no heat pits.

Scientific name *Lichanura trivirgata saslowi.*
Size 1m (39in).
Habitat Lava flows, rocky areas.
Distribution Mexico.
Food Birds, small mammals.
Breeding Live-bearing, litters of 3–8 young.

1m

JAVELIN SAND BOA

A snake with a short blunt tail, pale yellow, buff or grey in colour. The irregular markings along its back can be bars or spots. There is a dark line running from the eye to the corner of the jaw. There are no heat pits.

Scientific name *Eryx jaculus.*
Size 80cm (32in).
Habitat Dry, sandy places, under rocks.
Distribution SE Europe, Turkey, Middle East.
Food Rodents, small birds, lizards.
Breeding Live-bearing, litters up to 20.

80cm

GREEN TREE PYTHON

A green snake with a long prehensile tail and a broad head. There are rows of small white spots along the back. The young snakes are bright sulphur yellow or red, changing to green by the age of two. There are prominent heat pits.

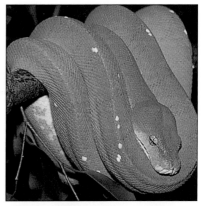

Scientific name *Chondropython viridis.*
Size 1.5m (5ft).
Habitat Rain forests.
Distribution New Guinea.
Food Birds, mammals, bats. Young eat lizards.
Breeding Egg-laying, up to 26 eggs.

CHILDREN'S PYTHON

This is one of the smaller pythons. The head is narrow and the body is slender. Light brown upperside, almost white underneath. The scales are large and cover the heat pits.

Scientific name *Liasis childreni.*
Size 1m (39in).
Habitat Plains and hills, near outcrops and woodland.
Distribution N Australia.
Food Small mammals, bats, frogs, lizards.
Breeding Egg-laying,8–16 eggs.

BLACK-HEADED PYTHON

A python with a glossy black head and neck. The rest of the body is yellowish, buff or pinkish-brown with dark cross-bars. There are no heat pits.

Scientific name *Aspidites melanocephalus.*
Size 2.6m (8^1/2ft).
Habitat Tropical and subtropical grasslands and hills.
Distribution Australia.
Food Snakes, birds on the ground, small mammals.
Breeding Egg-laying, 5–10 eggs.

2.6m

DIAMOND PYTHON

A snake that is usually black with a white spot on nearly every scale. Some areas can be completely black or white. There are heat pits around the mouth.

Scientific name *Morelia spilota spilota.*
Size 2m (6^1/2ft).
Habitat Woodland, rocky areas.
Distribution New South Wales, Australia.
Food Mammals, birds.
Breeding Egg-laying, up to 50 eggs.

2m

CARPET PYTHON

A variable snake, usually brown or grey with paler bands of colour crossing the body. There can be pale irregular blotches and streaks on the body. There is an almost black variety with yellow bands.

Scientific name *Morelia spilota variegata.*
Size 4m (13ft).
Habitat Forests, scrub, rocky areas.
Distribution Australia, New Guinea.
Food Mammals, birds.
Breeding Egg-laying, up to 50 eggs.

BURMESE PYTHON

A large yellowish python with large blotches of chestnut brown. There is an arrow-shaped dark mark on the top of its head and a dark streak through each eye. There are heat pits.

Scientific name *Python molurus bivittatus.*
Size 7m (23ft).
Habitat Tropical forests, fields.
Distribution India, Sri Lanka, Burma, Thailand.
Food Mammals, birds.
Breeding Egg-laying, up to 70 eggs.

ROYAL PYTHON

A strongly built python with a very dark background colour. There are oval blotches on the back which are tan, pale brown or yellowish-brown. Along each flank there are a series of light-coloured blotches. There are heat pits.

Scientific name *Python regius*.
Size 1.5m (5ft).
Habitat Grasslands and riverbanks.
Distribution W Africa.
Food Small mammals, birds.
Breeding Egg-laying, up to 10 eggs.

RETICULATED PYTHON

Possibly the largest snake in the world. They have intricate markings of black diamonds with yellow edges, on a grey background. There are also irregular white patches along the flanks. There are heat pits.

Scientific name *Python reticulatus*.
Size 10m (33ft).
Habitat Tropical forests and clearings, villages and towns.
Distribution SE Asia.
Food Mammals, birds, domestic livestock.
Breeding Egg-laying, up to 100 eggs.

AFRICAN PYTHON

A strong python with a wide head covered in scales. The colour can be brown or greenish-brown with a row of dark markings on the back and flanks. There are heat pits.

Scientific name *Python sebae*.
Size 5m (16ft).
Habitat Grasslands, rocky areas near villages and farms.
Distribution S Sahara in Africa.
Food Mammals, birds, crocodiles, fish.
Breeding Egg-laying, up to 50 eggs.

LONG NOSE TREE SNAKE

A very thin snake with an elongated head and a pointed snout. The eyes have horizontal pupils which allow the snake to judge distances accurately. The green colour, along with the shape, provide efficient camouflage.

Scientific name *Ahaetulla nasuta*.
Size 2m (6^1/2ft).
Habitat Tropical forests.
Distribution SE Asia.
Food Lizards, frogs, small mammals.
Breeding Live-bearing, small litters.

TRANS-PECOS RATSNAKE

A ratsnake with a slim body, narrow head and large eyes. The colour can vary from tan, to buff or cream to pale yellow. There are dark markings along the back. They are active only at night.

Scientific name *Bogertrophis subocularis*.
Size 1.6m (5^1/4ft).
Habitat Deserts, rocky semi-arid places.
Distribution USA, Mexico.
Food Small mammals, snakes, lizards.
Breeding Egg-laying, up to 20 eggs.

1.6m

GLOSSY SNAKE

A slender snake with an almost cylindrical body and smooth shiny scales. There are pale brown or grey markings. The ground colour can be pale tan, cream or brown. They are docile snakes and do not bite.

Scientific name *Arizona elegans*.
Size 1.5m (5ft).
Habitat Grassland, scrub, open woods, deserts.
Distribution USA, Mexico.
Food Small mammals, snakes, lizards.
Breeding Egg-laying, up to 20 eggs.

1.5m

PARADISE FLYING TREE SNAKE

Each scale is black with a yellow-green centre. There are also some dark red markings along the back. A slender snake also known as the 'flying snake' as it can parachute from high branches by spreading out its ribs.

Scientific name *Chrysopelea paradisii*.
Size 1m (39in).
Habitat Forests, gardens, trees and shrubs.
Distribution SE Asia.
Food Lizards, frogs, small rodents.
Breeding Egg-laying.

DARK GREEN WHIPSNAKE

A slim snake with large eyes. They are usually green or yellow with irregular dark crossbars on the back and sides. The tail area has broken stripes. There are some areas where these snakes are all black.

Scientific name *Coluber viridflavus*.
Size 2m (6¹/2ft).
Habitat Dry, rocky areas, woods and fields.
Distribution Central Europe, Italy.
Food Lizards, small mammals, nestling birds.
Breeding Egg-laying.

SMOOTH SNAKE

A cylindrical snake with smooth scales.
The head and the eyes are small. The
colour is usually grey with small brown
spots running down the back. Mostly
active by day, it kills its prey by
constriction.

Scientific name *Coronella austriaca*.
Size 75cm (30in).
Habitat Heaths, open woods, railway
embankments.
Distribution Europe, W Asia.
Food Lizards, small rodents.
Breeding Live-bearing, up to 10 young.

AFRICAN EGG-EATING SNAKE

A slim snake with keeled scales and a
cylindrical body. The head is small with
two V-shaped marks. The snout is very
rounded. It is grey in colour with large
dark blotches along the back. The
inside of the mouth is black.

Scientific name *Dasypeltis scabra*.
Size 1m (39in).
Habitat Most areas, except deserts.
Distribution Africa, S of the Sahara.
Food Bird's eggs, swallowed whole,
crushed and the empty shell rejected.
Breeding Egg-laying, up to 25 eggs.

AMERICAN RACER

A slender, fast moving snake with smooth scales. The colours include black, blue, grey, greenish, olive and brown, making this a difficult snake to identify. They are active by day.

Scientific name *Coluber constrictor*.
Size 1.5m (5ft).
Habitat Fields, lake edges.
Distribution N and Central America.
Food Reptiles, birds and small mammals.
Breeding Egg-laying, up to 20 eggs.

1.5m

SCARLET SNAKE

A burrowing snake with a cylindrical body. The head is pointed and small with smooth scales. It is brightly coloured with bands of red, white and black on the back. The underside is white or cream.

Scientific name *Cemophora Coccinea*.
Size 40cm (16in).
Habitat Loose, sandy soil. Old logs.
Distribution SE USA.
Food Snakes and their eggs, lizards, mice.
Breeding Egg-laying.

40cm

RINGNECK SNAKE

A small, slim snake whose body is light grey to black. Behind the head, there is a yellow or orange band. The belly is orange and the tail is red underneath which is held up when frightened.

Scientific name *Diadophis punctatus.*
Size 75cm (30in).
Habitat Damp areas. Under logs.
Distribution N America.
Food Worms, amphibians, insects, small reptiles slugs.
Breeding Egg-laying.

INDIGO SNAKE

A large, black snake with polished scales. The body is almost triangular. The chin can be red or dull white. The young snakes have more red on their undersides and bluish marks on their sides.

Scientific name *Drymarchon corais couperi.*
Size 2m (6¹/2ft).
Habitat Sandy areas.
Distribution SE USA (Florida).
Food Fish, amphibians, reptiles, birds, small mammals.
Breeding Egg-laying, up to 10 eggs.

BLACK RAT SNAKE

These are shiny, black snakes. There are nine subspecies recognised, all have variable colouring and markings. The young sometimes keep the patterning they are born with – greyish with darker markings down their bodies.

Scientific name *Elaphe obsoleta*.
Size 1.8m(6ft).
Habitat Savannah, trees.
Distribution N America to Mexico.
Food Small mammals, birds, rodents.
Breeding Egg-laying, up to 14 eggs.

CORN SNAKE

A handsome ratsnake with large red saddles on a grey or yellowish ground. There is a black border on each saddle and smaller spots on the flanks and there is always a V-shaped mark on the top of the head. The underside is black and white.

Scientific name *Elaphe guttata guttata*.
Size 1.8m (6ft).
Habitat Woody or rocky areas. Good climbers.
Distribution SE and E USA.
Food Rodents, birds.
Breeding Egg-laying, up to 20 eggs.

FOX SNAKE

A strongly built ratsnake with bold patterning of dark chestnut-brown blotches down the back. The background is either grey or yellowish. There are smaller blotches on the flanks. The head may be rust-coloured.

Scientific name *Elaphe vulpina*.
Size 1.3m (51in).
Habitat Prairies, woods, swamps, farmland.
Distribution Central USA, Canada.
Food Small mammals.
Breeding Egg-laying.

WESTERN HOGNOSE SNAKE

This snake has a distinct snout which is upturned. The scales are heavily keeled, giving a rough appearance. The colour is usually light brown or grey with blotches of brown, reddish-brown or olive along the back. When frightened, it can pretend to be dead.

Scientific name *Herterodon nasicus*.
Size 70cm (28in).
Habitat Prairies, sandy soil.
Distribution USA, Canada, Mexico.
Food Rodents, amphibians.
Breeding Egg-laying, up to 15 eggs.

EASTERN HOGNOSE SNAKE

Similar to the Western Hognose Snake but with several different colour patterns. The colour is usually brown or tan with blotches on the back and sides. Some species are pure black. The snake can play dead when threatened.

Scientific name *Heterodon paltyrhinos.*
Size 80cm (32in).
Habitat Sandy soil areas.
Distribution Central, E and SE USA.
Food Rodents, amphibians.
Breeding Egg-laying.

SPOTTED NIGHT SNAKE

This is a small snake with smooth scales. The head is flattish and there are dark blotches along the back. The snake is light brown or grey in colour. Behind the head, there is often a large dark patch, which can be divided into two areas. Active only at night.

Scientific name Hypsiglena torquata.
Size 60cm (24in).
Habitat Desert, scrub, meadows, woods.
Distribution S and SW USA.
Food Amphibians, small mammals.
Breeding Egg-laying, 2–9 eggs.

VIPERINE SNAKE

Young snakes are slender, adults are stockily built. The scales are keeled. The colour can be olive, brown, greenish or reddish with two rows of dark blotches on the back. There may also be two pale yellow stripes down the back.

Scientific name *Natrix maura*.
Size 75cm (30in).
Habitat Close to water.
Distribution Spain, Portugal, N Africa.
Food Frogs, toads, tadpoles, earthworms.
Breeding Egg-laying.

GRASS SNAKE

This snake has keeled scales and is usually olive-brown. There are black bars or spots on each side. There can be pale, yellow stripes on the body. Behind the head, there are cream or yellow patches which can form a collar distinguishing this from similar snakes.

Scientific name *Natrix natrix*.
Size 1.5m (5ft).
Habitat Damp meadows, banks of streams and canals, woods.
Distribution SW Asia, NW Africa, Europe.
Food Fish, amphibians.
Breeding Egg-laying, 20 eggs.

DICE SNAKE

A snake with heavily keeled scales and a narrow head. They are usually greenish, brown or grey, with spots over the back and sides. The nostrils and eyes point upwards.

Scientific name *Natrix tessellata.*
Size 1m (39in).
Habitat Often seen in water.
Distribution Italy, SE Europe, Asia.
Food Fish, amphibians.
Breeding Egg-laying.

GREEN WATER SNAKE

This snake has strongly keeled scales. The head is triangular and the small eyes point upwards. The colour is greenish-brown, with darker mottling.

Scientific name *Nerodia cyclopion.*
Size 1.3m (4^1/4ft).
Habitat Swamps, banks of lakes, ponds.
Distribution Florida, Mississippi Basin.
Food Fish, amphibians.
Breeding Live-bearing, up to 50 young.

SMOOTH GREEN SNAKE

A slim green snake with smooth scales. The colour is green on the surface and the undersides are white. The young can be olive or brown in colour.

Scientific name *Opheodryas vernalis.*
Size 50cm (20in).
Habitat Grassland, woods, fields.
Distribution N America.
Food Insects and spiders.
Breeding Egg-laying and live-bearing in some areas.

VINE SNAKE

This snake has an elongated head and pointed snout. The colour can be grey or brown, paler nearer the head. There is a dark line through the eye and a dark area on top of the head.

Scientific name *Oxybelis aeneus.*
Size 1.5m (5ft).
Habitat Forest, scrub, trees.
Distribution S Arizona, S America, Mexico.
Food Lizards, amphibians.
Breeding Egg-laying, 3–5 eggs.

BULL SNAKE

A powerful snake with very keeled scales. The snout is pointed. There is a dark line running through each eye. The colour is yellowish-brown with blotches which are either brown or rust-coloured. If disturbed, this snake will hiss and may bite.

Scientific name *Pittuophis melanoleucus sayi.*
Size 2.5m (8^1/4ft).
Habitat Deserts, prairies, farmland.
Distribution N America to Mexico.
Food Small mammals, birds.
Breeding Egg-laying, up to 24 eggs.

2.5m

COMMON GARTER SNAKE

This species occurs farther north than any other snake in the New World. In the northernmost parts of its territory, it often congregates in huge numbers when hibernating.

Scientific name *Thamnophis sirtalis.*
Size 1.3m (51in).
Habitat Farmland, prairies, near water.
Distribution N America.
Food Fish, ampihibians, earthworms.
Breeding Live-bearing, 7–85 young.

1.3m

TERRESTRIAL GARTER SNAKE

A large stocky snake, with keeled scales. The markings can vary, but there is often a stripe along the back and on the flanks. Between the stripes, the area can either be spotted and pale, or dark with white blotches.

Scientific name *Thamnophis elegans.*
Size 1m (39in).
Habitat Grasslands, wooded areas, fields.
Distribution W USA.
Food Rodents, amphibians.
Breeding Live-bearing, 4–15 young.

WESTERN RIBBON SNAKE

A very slim snake with an orange stripe down the middle of the back. There is a cream or pale yellow stripe on each flank. The colour of the area between the stripes is usually brown or olive. The area around the mouth has light coloured scales.

Scientific name *Thamnophis proximus.*
Size 1.2m (47in).
Habitat Woodlands, marshes, lakesides, tropical forests.
Distribution Gulf coast USA, Mexico, Mississippi valley, C America.
Food Fish, frogs, insects, earthworms.
Breeding Live-bearing, 4–27 young.

DEATH ADDER

A bite from this snake can prove lethal to humans. This snake resembles a viper with a broad, triangular head, a short tail and lightly keeled scales. The colour varies from grey, to red or brown, There are some crossbands over the body.

Scientific name *Acanthophis antarcticus.*
Size 50cm (20in).
Habitat Dry, rocky places.
Distribution Australia.
Food Small mammals, birds, reptiles.
Breeding Live-bearing, up to 20 young.

50cm

BANDED KRAIT

A slim snake with a triangular cross-section to its body. Its head is narrow and the scales are smooth. The banded pattern alternates between black and white or cream, in bands of almost equal width. The pattern runs from the neck to the tail.

Scientific name *Bungarus fasciatus.*
Size 2m (6^1/2ft).
Habitat Forests, fields.
Distribution SE Asia.
Food Other snakes.
Breeding Egg-laying.

2m

BLACK MAMBA

A powerful snake with smooth scales and a narrow head. The colour is dark grey, olive or brown – not black as the name would suggest. The head may have dark blotches and the mouth is black inside.

Scientific name *Dendroaspis polylepis.*
Size 2.5m (8¹/₄ft).
Habitat Scrub, grassland.
Distribution Africa, southern half.
Food Small mammals, birds.
Breeding Egg-laying, 12–14 eggs.

2.5m

TEXAS CORAL SNAKE

This snake is slim with smooth, shiny scales. The snout is black and there is a wide yellow band across the head. The rest of the body has red and black bands, separated by yellow bands.

Scientific name *Micrurus fulvius.*
Size 75cm (30in).
Habitat Sandy soil areas. Under logs.
Distribution SE USA, Mexico.
Food Snakes, lizards, small mammals.
Breeding Egg-laying, 3–5 eggs.

75cm

RINKALS or SPITTING COBRA

This snake can be marked with black bands on a grey, yellow or orange background. It can also be plain black or brown with specks of a paler colour. When frightened, it rears up and spreads it hood out.

Scientific name *Hemachatus hemachatus.*
Size 1m (39in).
Habitat Grassland.
Distribution S Africa.
Food Small mammals, birds, frogs, toads, reptiles.
Breeding Live-bearing, up to 63 young.

INDIAN OR SPECTACLED COBRA

This snake has smooth scales and varies in colour. They are usually black or dark brown, with lighter marks on the throat. When alarmed, it spreads out its hood very wide and can display a white mark, shaped like a 'spectacle', on the back.

Scientific name *Naja naja.*
Size 2m (6¹/2ft).
Habitat Outskirts of villages and towns, farmland, forests.
Distribution India, Pakistan, Sri Lanka.
Food Small mammals, reptiles.
Breeding Egg-laying.

TIGER SNAKE

A snake with smooth scales. The colour can be grey, olive or even reddish and there can be lighter crossbands. When alarmed, it can flatten out its neck, though they are normally a placid snake.

Scientific name *Notechis scutatus.*
Size 1.2m (47in).
Habitat Forests, grassland.
Distribution SE Australia.
Food Frogs and small mammals
Breeding Live-bearing, up to 100 young.

TAIPAN

A long snake with either smooth or keeled scales. The colour can be either light or dark brown, which pales on the underside and flanks. The head is often a lighter colour and can be cream.

Scientific name *Oxyuranus scutellatus.*
Size 2m (6¹/2ft).
Habitat Woodland, grassland, forests.
Distribution Australia, New Guinea.
Food Small mammals.
Breeding Egg-laying, 2–20 eggs.

FIERCE SNAKE

One of the most dangerous and
venomous snakes in the world, though a
rare species. A graceful snake with
smooth scales, and large eyes. It is
coloured brown or olive and can have
dark marks on the head. Similar to the
Taipan but more deadly.

Scientific name *Oxyuranus
microlepidotus.*
Size 2m (6¹/2ft).
Habitat Grassland, outback.
Distribution Central Australia.
Food Small mammals.
Breeding Egg Laying, 12–20 eggs.

WESTERN BROWN SNAKE

A whip-like snake with a narrow head.
The colour varies considerably between
light brown to black, and from solid
colours to banded or crossbars.
Combinations of these markings are
also possible.

Scientific name *Pseudonaja nuchalis.*
Size 1.5m (5ft).
Habitat Forests, grasslands, deserts.
Distribution Australia.
Food Small mammals, reptiles.
Breeding Egg-laying.

BANDY BANDY

This is a burrowing venomous snake only found on the surface at night. The scales are smooth on this slim snake. The colour is mainly black with white rings around the body and tail and across the head.

Scientific name *Vermicella annulata.*
Size 60cm (24in).
Habitat Wooded grasslands and scrub.
Distribution Australia.
Food Other snakes.
Breeding Egg-laying.

PELAGIC SEA SNAKE

A very distinctive sea snake, which has hexagonal, non-overlapping scales. The head is elongated and the tail appears flattened. The colour is a bright yellow with a dark line running along the back. They can be found in huge shoals in warm seas.

Scientific name *Pelamis platurus.*
Size 70cm (28in).
Habitat Marine.
Distribution African coast, S America, C America.
Food Fish.
Breeding Live-bearing.

PUFF ADDER

A stocky snake with a wide, triangular head. The scales are very keeled and it has a short tail. The colour can be brown or yellowish, with black chevron-shaped markings down the back. There is a white edge to each chevron. Markings can be indistinct.

Scientific name *Bitis arietans*.
Size 1m (39in).
Habitat Most areas, except deserts.
Distribution Africa.
Food Small mammals, birds.
Breeding Live-bearing, 20–40 young.

GABOON VIPER

A very large and stockily built snake. The head is broad, flat and triangular with small eyes. The patterning is geometric, made up of rectangles, triangles and diamonds. These act as camouflage on the forest floor. The colours can be buff, purple, pink and varieties of brown. Dangerous and venomous.

Scientific name *Bitis gabonica*.
Size 1.2m (47in).
Habitat Forests.
Distribution Africa.
Food Medium mammals, birds.
Breeding Live-bearing, up to 60 young.

RHINOCEROS VIPER

A stocky snake with heavily keeled scales. There are also horn-like scales on the snout. The colouring is made up of bluish-green, bow-tie marks on a purplish background. The sides are paler with marks edged in yellow.

Scientific name *Bitis nasicornis.*
Size 1m (39in).
Habitat Forests, riverbanks.
Distribution W Africa.
Food Small mammals, birds.
Breeding Live-bearing.

NOSE-HORNED VIPER

A large viper with a fleshy horn on the snout. The scales are keeled and it is silvery-grey, brown or orange in colour. There are darker zigzag markings which can appear to be separate blotches.

Scientific name *Vipera ammodytes.*
Size 1m (39in).
Habitat Drystone walls, meadows, rocky areas.
Distribution Turkey, SE Europe.
Food Small mammals, birds.
Breeding Live-bearing, up to 10 young.

ADDER

A sturdy viper with some large scales on its head. There are keeled scales on the body. Males are grey with dark grey or black zigzag running down the back. Females are brown or reddish with a dark zigzag. Some species are pure black.

Scientific name *Vipera berus.*
Size 70cm (28in).
Habitat Bogs, woods, fields, heaths.
Distribution Europe, Asia.
Food Lizards, small rodents.
Breeding Live-bearing, up to 10 young.

RUSSELL'S VIPER

A stocky snake which is pale grey-brown. There are dark brown ovals along the back which are edged in white. More ovals can be seen on the sides in an alternating pattern to those on the back.

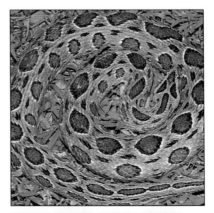

Scientific name *Vipera russelli.*
Size 1m (39in).
Habitat Grasslands, plantations.
Distribution Pakistan, Burma, India, Sri Lanka.
Food Small mammals.
Breeding Live-bearing, up to 65 young.

LATASTE'S VIPER

A stoutly built viper with keeled scales.
There is a fleshy horn on the snout. The
colour is grey or pale brown with a
zigzag line running down the back.
Down the sides, there are dark blotches.

Scientific name *Vipera latasti*.
Size 60cm (24in).
Habitat Hillsides which are stony, or
sandy coastal places.
Distribution Spain, Portugal, Africa.
Food Small mammals, birds, lizards.
Breeding Live-bearing.

CANTIL

A viper with a long tail. The head is
triangular with a white line running from
the nose to the jaw. Another white line
crosses the eyes. The body may be black
or dark brown and there are wide bands
of paler brown edged in white.

Scientific name *Agkistrodon
bilineatus*.
Size 1m (39in).
Habitat Scrub and forests.
Distribution Mexico.
Food Rodents.
Breeding Live-bearing, up to 10 young.

COPPERHEAD

This snake has keeled scales and a triangular head. The patterns are formed from bands of buff, pink or tan, alternating with bands of red, or brown. The tail may be tipped yellow in young snakes.

Scientific name *Agkistrodon contortrix.*
Size 75cm (30in).
Habitat Rocky hillsides, swamps.
Distribution SE USA (not Florida), Mexico.
Food Rodents, small birds, frogs.
Breeding Live-bearing, up to 8 young.

COTTONMOUTH

A large snake with keeled scales. There are crossbands within the brown, grey or black colouration. There can also be e thin white line from the snout to above the eye.

Scientific name *Agkistrodon piscivorus.*
Size 1.25m (49in).
Habitat Rivers, ditches, swamps, lakes.
Distribution SE USA.
Food Fish, frogs, salamanders, small mammals, birds.
Breeding Live-bearing, 3–12 young.

EYELASH VIPER

This is a tree dwelling snake which gets its name from a cluster of scales over each eye. A slim snake with very keeled scales. The colour varies between yellow and green with brown marks resembling lichen.

Scientific name *Bothriopsis schlegelii*.
Size 60cm (24in).
Habitat Tropical rain forests.
Distribution S America.
Food Small birds, lizards, mammals.
Breeding Live-bearing.

STRIPED PALM VIPER

This pit viper has keeled scales and a wonderful colour scheme. The head and neck are bluish-green with white spots or crossbars on the back. The young snakes are brown with black and white marks, before they alter to adult colouration.

Scientific name *Bothriechis lateralis*.
Size 70cm (28in).
Habitat Tropical forests.
Distribution Costa Rica, Panama.
Food Lizards, frogs, small mammals.
Breeding Live-bearing.

EASTERN DIAMONDBACK RATTLESNAKE

A large rattlesnake with a broad, rounded head. The colouring can be brown or olive with large, outlined diamonds down the back. The face has two coloured streaks.

Scientific name *Crotalus adamanteus*.
Size 1.7m (67in).
Habitat Pinewoods and palm scrub.
Distribution Florida.
Food Small mammals.
Breeding Live-bearing.

WESTERN DIAMONDBACK RATTLESNAKE

This large rattlesnake has a rounded snout. The diamonds on their backs are edged in a lighter colour. The background colour may be grey, bluish, pink or black. On the face, there are two light streaks, with a darker area in between.

Scientific name *Crotalus atrox*.
Size 1.7m (67in).
Habitat Dry desert, grassland.
Distribution SW USA, N Mexico.
Food Rabbits, squirrels, rodents, birds.
Breeding Live-bearing, up to 40 young.

SOUTH AMERICAN RATTLESNAKE

This snake has a variety of species, colours and markings. The colours range from light grey, brown, yellow and tan, to greenish-grey olive and black. Several have diamond pattering on their backs, edged in yellow or white.

Scientific name *Crotalus durissus.*
Size 1.5m (5ft).
Habitat Dry forests, grassland.
Distribution Mexico to Argentina.
Food Mammals, birds.
Breeding Live-bearing.

1.5m

BLACK TAILED RATTLESNAKE

This snake has a varying pattern. It can be greenish, yellow, tan, orange or brown with diamonds along the back. The tail is black and there may be a black mark over the face.

Scientific name *Crotalus molossus.*
Size 1m (39in).
Habitat Semi-desert, scrub, woods.
Distribution S USA, Central Mexico.
Food Small mammals, birds.
Breeding Live-bearing, 3–6 young.

1m

RED DIAMONDBACK RATTLESNAKE

A slender rattlesnake with large, white edged, diamonds on its back. The colours can be brick-red, reddish-brown or orange. The tail has black and white rings before the rattle.

Scientific name *Crotalus ruber.*
Size 1m (39in).
Habitat Deserts.
Distribution California, Mexico.
Food Small mammals, birds.
Breeding Live-bearing, 3–20 young.

MOJAVE RATTLESNAKE

A medium-sized rattlesnake often mistaken for other species. There are oval or diamond marks on the back. A light-coloured stripe runs from the eye to the mouth.

Scientific name *Crotalus scutulatus.*
Size 1m (39in).
Habitat Deserts, dry scrub, rocky places.
Distribution SW USA, central Mexico.
Food Small mammals.
Breeding Live-bearing, 2–11 young.

WESTERN RATTLESNAKE

There are several varieties of this snake. They all have a row of dark blotches on the back, which can be olive, brown or black. The background can be grey, cream, light green or buff.

Scientific name *Crotalus viridis*.
Size 1.5m (5ft).
Habitat Deserts, forests, prairies.
Distribution W USA, N Mexico.
Food Small mammals, birds, reptiles.
Breeding Live-bearing, up to 25 young.

1.5m

TIMBER RATTLESNAKE

Found in the Appalachians, this snake is one of the most common North American rattlesnakes. They may overwinter in large numbers in northern areas with other rat snakes. Colours vary between yellow or tan background with dark crossbars and a dusky black with little patterning.

Scientific name *Crotalus horridus*.
Size 1.2m (47in).
Habitat Rocky slopes, wooded valleys.
Distribution Canada, USA.
Food Rodents, chipmunks.
Breeding Live-bearing.

1.2m

P I T   V I P E R S

WHITE-LIPPED PIT VIPER

A tree-living viper with a pale green colour and orange eyes with vertical pupils. Yellowish-green underneath. There is a white line, along each side, in the male, which is absent in the female.

Scientific name *Trimeresurus albolabris.*
Size 70cm (28in).
Habitat Tropical forests.
Distribution NE India, SE China.
Food Lizards, frogs, rodents.
Breeding Live-bearing.

WAGLER'S PIT VIPER

A distinctively coloured, tree dwelling, pit viper. Adults are black with green spots, and green scales, edged in black on the sides. The young are green with red and white spots. The head is spade-shaped and black with yellowish-green streaks.

Scientific name *Tropidolaemus wagleri.*
Size 1m (39in).
Habitat Tropical forests.
Distribution Thailand, Indonesia, Malaysia, Philippines.
Food Lizards, frogs, small mammals.
Breeding Live-bearing.

Index   Index of common names

INDEX

Index Index of scientific names

I N D E X